BoE 4060

Children's Christmas Piano

Das Kinder-Weihnachtsalbum mit den beliebtesten und bekanntesten Weihnachtsliedern in sehr leichter bis leichter Fassung für Klavier/Keyboard.

A Children's Christmas Book containing the most popular Christmas songs and carols in easy and very easy arrangements for piano and keyboard.

- Für meine lieben Töchter Sarah und Laura -

- For Sarah and Laura, my daughters -

VORWORT

Liebe Kinder,

in diesem Spielheft CHILDREN'S CHRISTMAS PIANO findet Ihr jede Menge Weihnachtslieder, und die meisten davon kennt Ihr bestimmt.

Wenn Ihr fleißig seid und viele Lieder einübt, könnt Ihr Eure Familie zu Weihnachten mit einem tollen Konzert überraschen.

Wer einen Kassettenrecorder hat, kann sein Konzert ja auch auf Kassette aufnehmen und es denen zu Weihnachten schenken, die nicht mit Euch feiern können.

Doch nun viel Freude beim Spielen der Weihnachtslieder und

FRÖHLICHE WEIHNACHTEN

wünscht Euch
HANS-GÜNTER HEUMANN

Hinweis für Keyboard-Spieler:

● Spiele die rechte Hand sämtlicher Stücke wie notiert.

● Die linke Hand spielt nach den angegebenen Akkordsymbolen oberhalb des Notensystems, entweder als *'fingered chords'* (gegriffene Akkorde) oder als *'single fingered chords'* - SFC - (Einfingerbegleitautomatik).

FOREWORD

Dear young Pianists,

in this volume CHILDREN'S CHRISTMAS PIANO, you will find lots of Christmas songs and carols, some of which you will certainly recognise.

If you are really hard working and practise many of the songs, you could surprise your family at Christmas with a splendid recital.

If you own a cassette recorder, why not tape your recital and make a gift of it to those who cannot be with you for Christmas?

Whatever, have fun playing these carols and songs and have a

HAPPY CHRISTMAS

from me,
HANS-GÜNTER HEUMANN

Attention Keyboarders!

● Play the right hand part throughout as written.

● If the left hand is playing from the chord symbols above the stave, either *'fingered chords'* or *'single fingered chords'* - SFC - will do.

Titelgestaltung: MAREK MANN
Illustrationen: OLGA BLUMENBERG

BOSWORTH EDITION

CHILDREN'S CHRISTMAS PIANO
Inhalt/Contents

Stille Nacht, heilige Nacht *)

SILENT NIGHT, HOLY NIGHT

SEHR LEICHT/ VERY EASY

Worte: Joseph Mohr

Weise) Franz Xaver Gruber
Melody
Arr.: Hans-Günter Heumann

Andante M.M. ♩ = 96-100

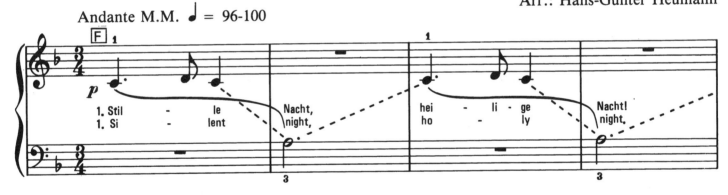

1. Stil - le Nacht, hei - li - ge Nacht!
1. Si - lent night, ho - ly night!

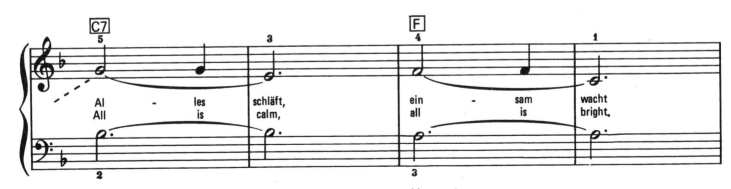

Al - les schläft, ein - sam wacht
All is calm, all is bright,

*) Dieses wohl bekannteste Weihnachtslied wird in allen Sprachen von den Menschen gesungen, die ein christliches Weihnachtsfest feiern. Es wurde einige Tage vor Weihnachten 1818 in Oberndorf bei Salzburg vom Pfarrer Joseph Mohr und dem Organisten Franz Xaver Gruber geschrieben.

*) This carol, probably the most widely known of all, is sung throughout the world in every language by people in their millions celebrating Christmas. It dates back to a few days before Christmas in 1818 when it was composed and written by the church organist Franz Xaver Gruber and the priest Joseph Mohr at Oberndorf near Salzburg (Austria).

© Copyright MCMXCI by Bosworth & Co., Berlin
BOSWORTH & CO., BERLIN - LONDON

B. & Co. 24 982

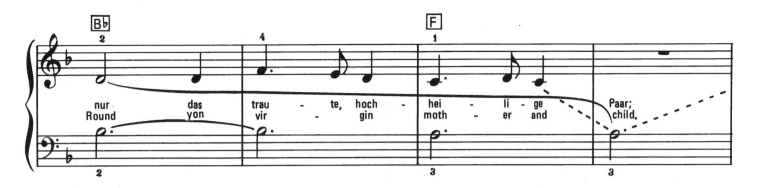

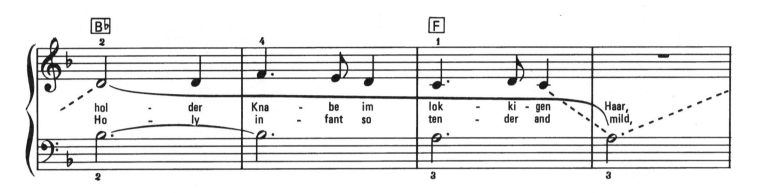

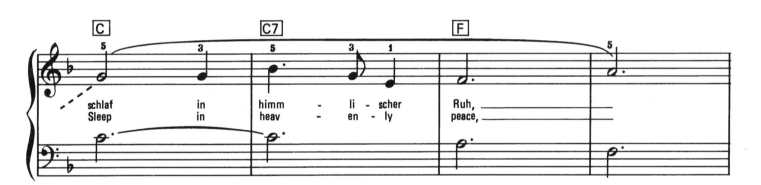

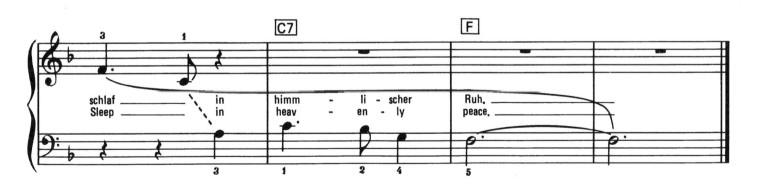

2. Stille Nacht, heilige Nacht! Hirten erst kundgemacht;
   durch der Engel Halleluja tönt es laut von fern und nah:
   Christ, der Retter, ist da! Christ, der Retter, ist da!

2. Silent night, holy night, Shepherds quake at the sight,
   Glories stream from heaven afar, Heav'nly hosts sing alleluia;
   Christ, the Saviour, is born! Christ, the Saviour, is born!

3. Stille Nacht, heilige Nacht! Gottes Sohn, o wie lacht
   Lieb aus deinem göttlichen Mund, da uns schlägt die rettende Stund,
   Christ, in deiner Geburt! Christ, in deiner Geburt!

3. Silent night, holy night, Son of God, love's pure light,
   Radiant beams from thy holy face, with the dawn of redeeming grace,
   Jesus, Lord, at thy birth, Jesus, Lord, at thy birth.

B. & Co. 24 982

Stille Nacht, heilige Nacht *⁾

SILENT NIGHT, HOLY NIGHT

Worte: Joseph Mohr

Weise ⎫ Franz Xaver Gruber
Melody ⎭

Arr.: Hans-Günter Heumann

Andante M.M. ♩ = 96-100

1. Stil - le Nacht, hei - li - ge Nacht!
1. Si - lent night, ho - ly night,

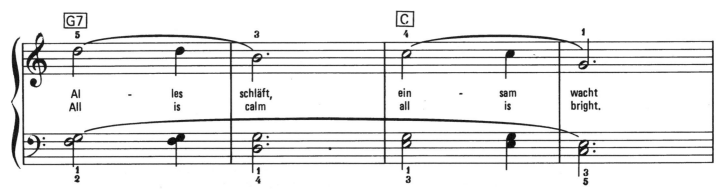

Al - les schläft, ein - sam wacht
All is calm, all is bright.

*⁾ Dieses wohl bekannteste Weihnachtslied wird in allen Sprachen von den Menschen gesungen, die ein christliches Weihnachtsfest feiern. Es wurde einige Tage vor Weihnachten 1818 in Oberndorf bei Salzburg vom Pfarrer Joseph Mohr und dem Organisten Franz Xaver Gruber geschrieben.

*⁾ This carol, probably the most widely known of all, is sung throughout the world in every language by people in their millions celebrating Christmas. It dates back to a few days before Christmas in 1818 when it was composed and written by the church organist Franz Xaver Gruber and the priest Joseph Mohr at Oberndorf near Salzburg (Austria).

2. Stille Nacht, heilige Nacht! Hirten erst kundgemacht;
   durch der Engel Halleluja tönt es laut von fern und nah:
   Christ, der Retter, ist da! Christ, der Retter, ist da!

2. Silent night, holy night, Shepherds quake at the sight,
   Glories stream from heaven afar, Heav'nly hosts sing alleluia;
   Christ, the Saviour, is born! Christ, the Saviour, is born!

3. Stille Nacht, heilige Nacht! Gottes Sohn, o wie lacht
   Lieb aus deinem göttlichen Mund, da uns schlägt die rettende Stund,
   Christ, in deiner Geburt! Christ, in deiner Geburt!

3. Silent night, holy night, Son of God, love's pure light,
   Radiant beams from thy holy face, with the dawn of redeeming grace,
   Jesus, Lord, at thy birth, Jesus, Lord, at thy birth.

O Tannenbaum, o Tannenbaum
O CHRISTMAS TREE, O CHRISTMAS TREE

Worte: August Zarnack / Ernst Anschütz

Volksweise aus dem 18. Jahrhundert
18th century folk melody
Arr.: Hans-Günter Heumann

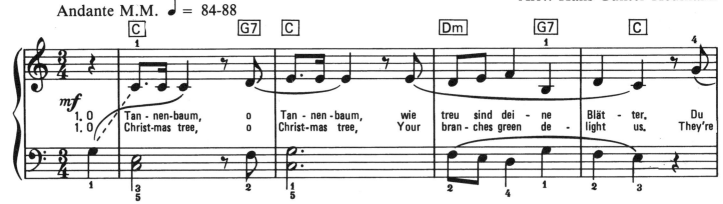

2. O Tannenbaum, o Tannenbaum,
du kannst mir sehr gefallen;
wie oft hat nicht zur Weihnachtszeit
ein Baum von dir mich hocherfreut!
O Tannenbaum, o Tannenbaum,
du kannst mir sehr gefallen.

3. O Tannenbaum, o Tannenbaum,
dein Kleid will mich was lehren:
Die Hoffnung und Beständigkeit
gibt Trost und Kraft zu jeder Zeit!
O Tannenbaum, o Tannenbaum,
das will dein Kleid mich lehren.

2. O Christmas tree, O Christmas tree,
You give us so much pleasure!
How oft at Christmas tide the sight,
Of green fir tree gives us delight!
O Christmas tree, O Christmas tree,
You give us so much pleasure!

3. O Christmas Tree! O Christmas Tree!
Thy candles shine so brightly!
From base to summit, gay and bright,
There's only splendor for the sight.
O Christmas Tree! O Christmas Tree!
Thy candles shine so brightly!

Angels from the Realms of Glory

GLORIA — HABEN ENGEL WIR VERNOMMEN

Textübertragung: Willi Träder

Weise aus Frankreich/ French Traditional
Arr.: Hans-Günter Heumann

2. Shepherds, in the field abiding, Watching o'er your flocks by night,
   God with man is now residing, Yonder shines the infant Light:
   Gloria in excelsis Deo, Gloria in excelsis Deo.

2. Sagt, ihr Hirten, welche Kunde weckt in euch der süße Klang,
   daß sich wie aus Engelsmunde hebet euer Lobgesang.
   Gloria in excelsis Deo! Gloria, Gloria in excelsis Deo!

3. Sages, leave your contemplations; Brighter visions beam afar:
   Seek the great Desire of Nations; Ye have seen his natal star:
   Gloria in excelsis Deo, Gloria in excelsis Deo.

3. Strahlt ein Stern vom Himmel nieder, alle Welt sieht seinen Schein;
   höret Gottes Botschaft wieder: Soll auf Erden Frieden sein.
   Gloria in excelsis Deo! Gloria, Gloria in excelsis Deo!

Aus: Gottfried Wolters „Ihr Hirten erwacht"
Möseler Verlag, Wolfenbüttel und Zürich

Jingle Bells

James Pierpont
Arr.: Hans-Günter Heumann

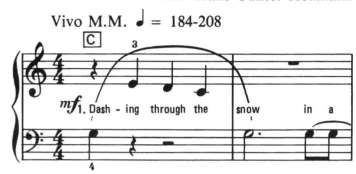

Vivo M.M. ♩ = 184-208

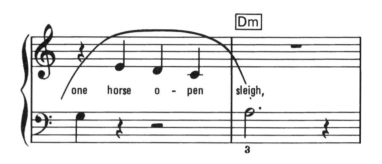

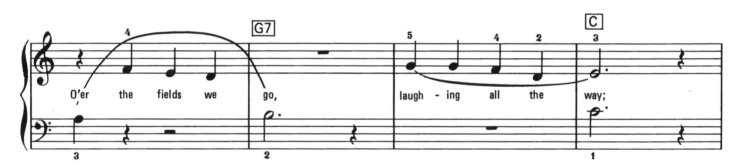

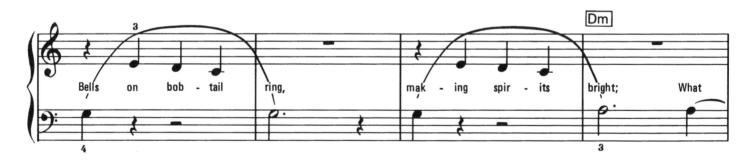

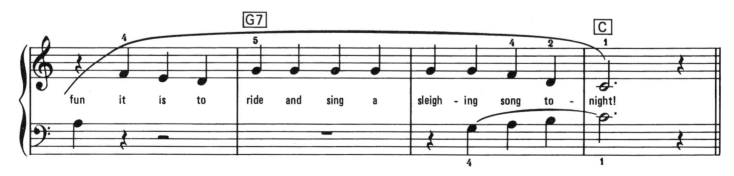

B. & Co. 24 982

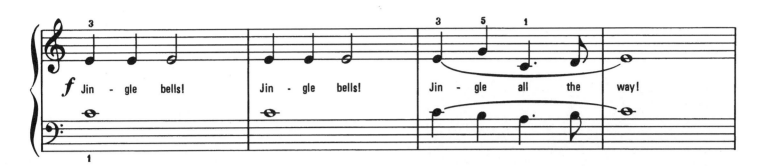

Jin - gle bells! Jin - gle bells! Jin - gle all the way!

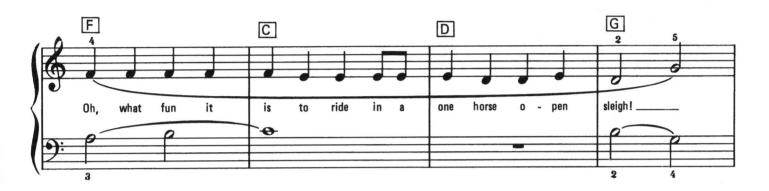

Oh, what fun it is to ride in a one horse o - pen sleigh! _____

Jin - gle bells! Jin - gle Bells! Jin - gle all the way!

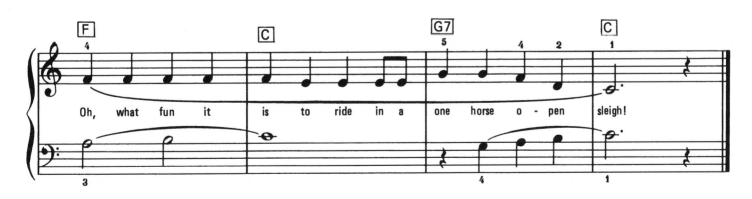

Oh, what fun it is to ride in a one horse o - pen sleigh!

2. Day or two ago I thought I'd take a ride,
   And soon Miss Fannie Bright Was seated by my side.
   The horse was lean and lank, Misfortune seem'd his lot,
   He got into a drifted bank, And we, we got up sot!
   Chorus

3. Now the ground is white, Go it while you're young;
   Take the girls tonight, And sing this sleighing song:
   Just get a bob-tailed nag, Two forty for his speed,
   Then hitch him to an open sleigh, And crack! you'll take the lead.
   Chorus

Jingle Bells

James Pierpont
Arr.: Hans-Günter Heumann

Vivo M.M. ♩ = 200-208

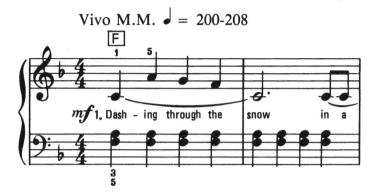

mf 1. Dash - ing through the snow in a

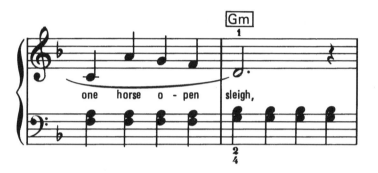

one horse o - pen sleigh,

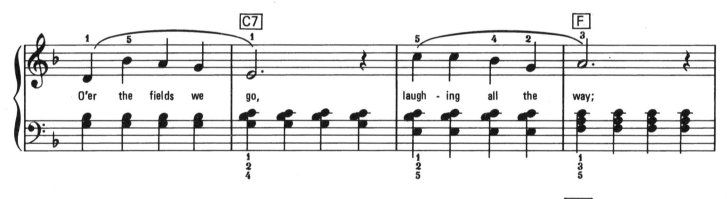

O'er the fields we go, laugh - ing all the way;

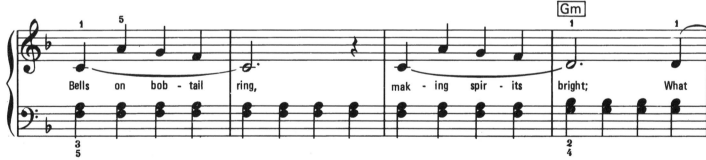

Bells on bob - tail ring, mak - ing spir - its bright; What

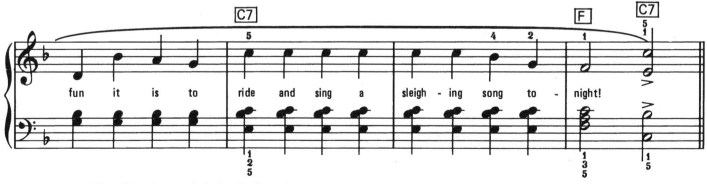

fun it is to ride and sing a sleigh - ing song to - night!

B. & Co. 24 982

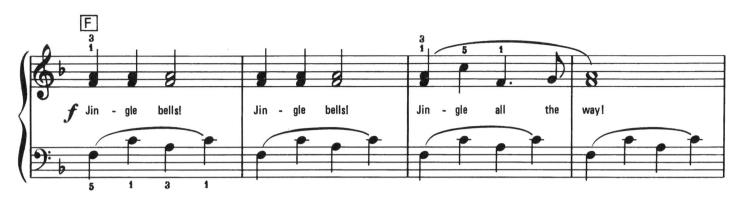

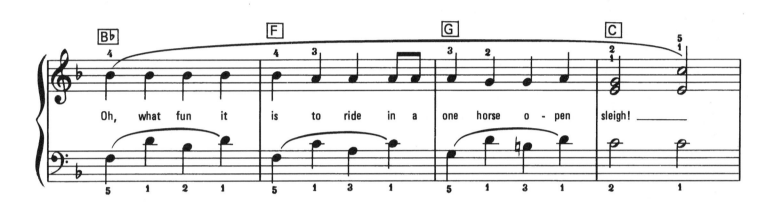

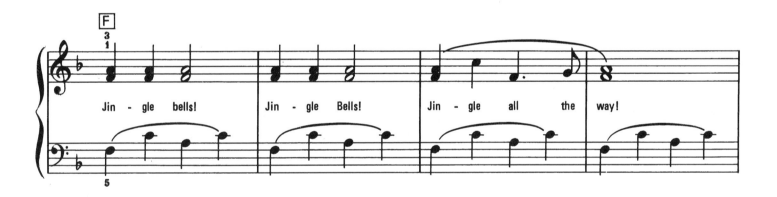

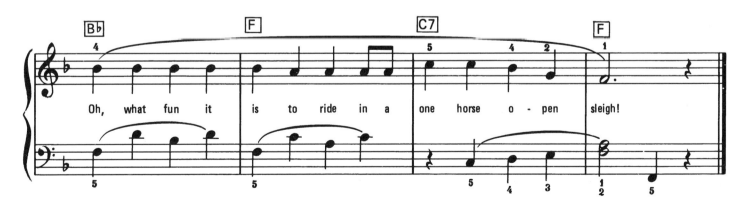

2. Day or two ago I thought I'd take a ride,
   And soon Miss Fannie Bright Was seated by my side.
   The horse was lean and lank, Misfortune seem'd his lot,
   He got into a drifted bank, And we, we got up sot!
   Chorus

3. Now the ground is white, Go it while you're young;
   Take the girls tonight, And sing this sleighing song:
   Just get a bob-tailed nag, Two forty for his speed,
   Then hitch him to an open sleigh, And crack! you'll take the lead.
   Chorus

Morgen, Kinder, wird's was geben

Worte: Karl Friedrich Splittegarb

Weise: Karl Gottlieb Hering
Arr.: Hans-Günter Heumann

Vivo M.M. ♩ = 208

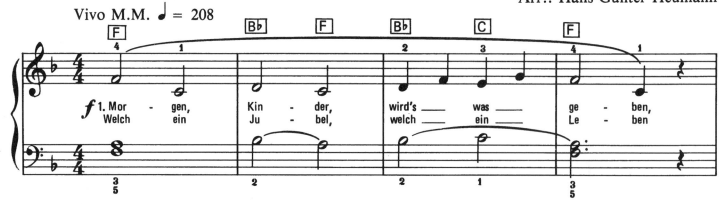

1. Mor - gen, Kin - der, wird's ___ was ___ ge - ben,
Welch ein Ju - bel, welch ___ ein ___ Le - ben

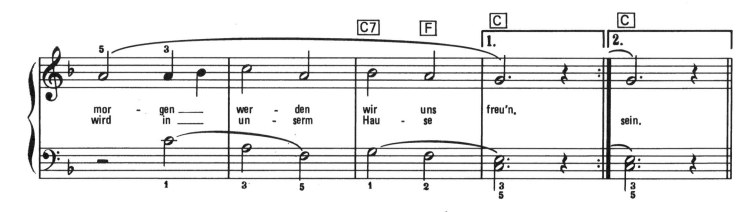

mor - gen ___ wer - den wir uns freu'n.
wird in ___ un - serm Hau - se sein.

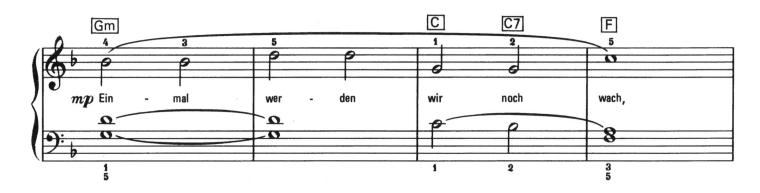

mp Ein - mal wer - den wir noch wach,

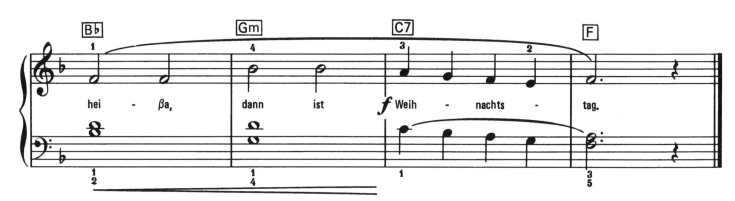

hei - βa, dann ist ƒ Weih - nachts - tag.

2. Wie wird dann die Stube glänzen von der großen Lichterzahl!
Schöner als bei frohen Tänzen ein geputzter Kronensaal.
Wißt ihr noch, wie vor'ges Jahr es am Heiligen Abend war?

3. Welch ein schöner Tag ist morgen, viele Freuden hoffen wir.
Unsre lieben Eltern sorgen lange, lange schon dafür.
O gewiß, wer sie nicht ehrt, ist der ganzen Lust nicht wert.

The First Nowell

English Traditional
Arr.: Hans-Günter Heumann

2. They looked up and saw a star,
Shining in the east, beyond them far,
And to the earth it gave great light,
And so it continued both day and night:
Nowell, Nowell, Nowell,
Born is the King of Israel!

3. This star drew nigh to the north-west,
O'er Bethlehem it took its rest,
And there it did both stop and stay,
Right over the place where Jesus lay:
Nowell, Nowell, Nowell,
Born is the King of Israel!

4. Then entered in those Wise Men three,
Full reverently upon their knee,
And offered there in his presence,
Their gold and myrrh, and frankincense.
Nowell, Nowell, Nowell,
Born is the King of Israel!

Morgen kommt der Weihnachtsmann

16

Worte: A. H. Hoffmann von Fallersleben

Aus dem Französischen (17. Jahrh.)
17th Century French Traditional
Arr.: Hans-Günter Heumann

Allegetto M.M. ♩ = 120-126

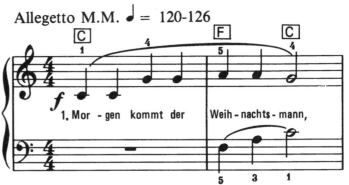

1. Mor - gen kommt der Weih - nachts - mann,

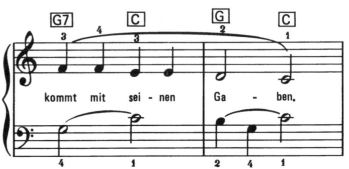

kommt mit sei - nen Ga - ben.

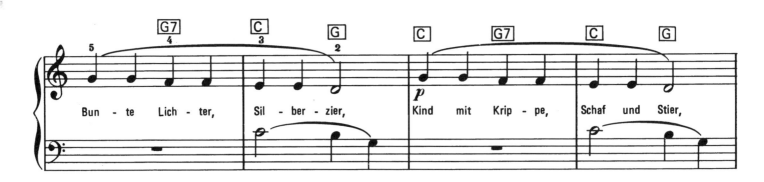

Bun - te Lich - ter, Sil - ber - zier, Kind mit Krip - pe, Schaf und Stier,

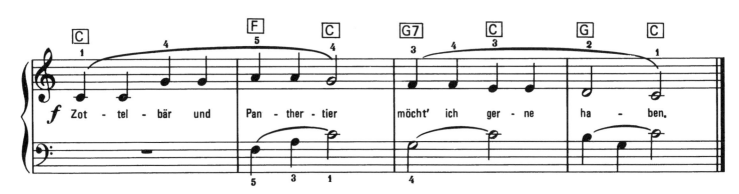

Zot - tel - bär und Pan - ther - tier möcht' ich ger - ne ha - ben.

2. Morgen kommt der Weihnachtsmann, kommt mit seinen Gaben.
Puppen, Pferdchen, Sang und Spiel, und auch sonst der Freude viel,
ja, o welch ein Glücksgefühl, könnt' ich alles haben.

3. Doch du weißt ja unsern Wunsch, kennst ja unsre Herzen.
Kinder, Vater und Mama, auch sogar der Großpapa,
alle, alle sind wir da, warten dein mit Schmerzen.

O du fröhliche, o du selige

Worte: Johannes Daniel Falk (1816)

Sizilianisches Volkslied/Sicilian Trad.
Arr.: Hans-Günter Heumann

Moderato M.M. ♩ = 108-112

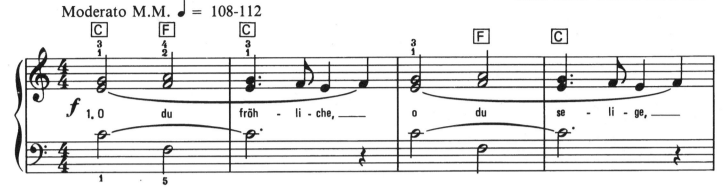

1. O du fröh - li - che, ___ o du se - li - ge,

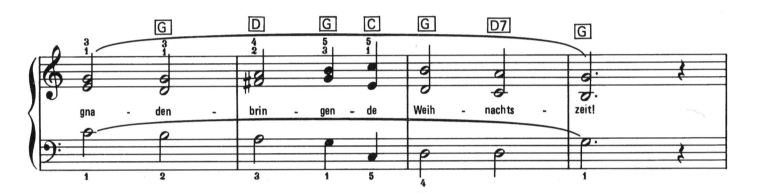

gna - den - brin - gen - de Weih - nachts - zeit!

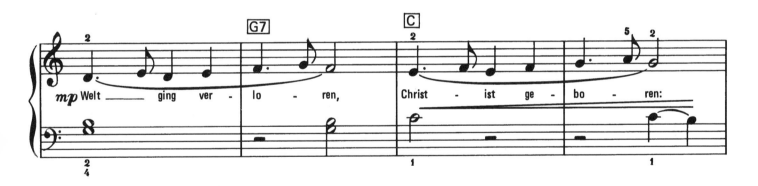

Welt ___ ging ver - lo - ren, Christ - ist ge - bo - ren:

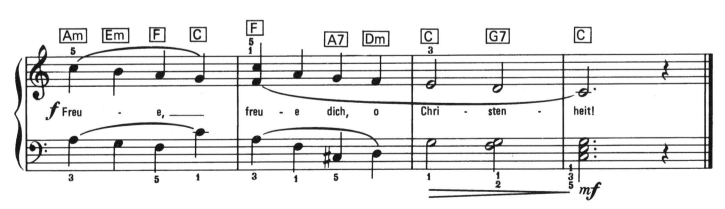

Freu - e, ___ freu - e dich, o Chri - sten - heit!

2. O du fröhliche, o du selige, gnadenbringende Weihnachtszeit!
Christ ist erschienen, uns zu versühnen:
Freue, freue dich, o Christenheit!

3. O du fröhliche, o du selige, gnadenbringende Weihnachtszeit!
Himmlische Heere jauchzen dir Ehre:
Freue, o freue dich, o Christenheit!

Herbei, o ihr Gläubigen

O COME, ALL YE FAITHFUL

Aus dem lateinischen "Adeste fideles"
Worte von Heinrich Ranke (1798-1876)

Aus Portugal (um 1815)
Portuguese Traditional (app. 1815)
Arr.: Hans-Günter Heumann

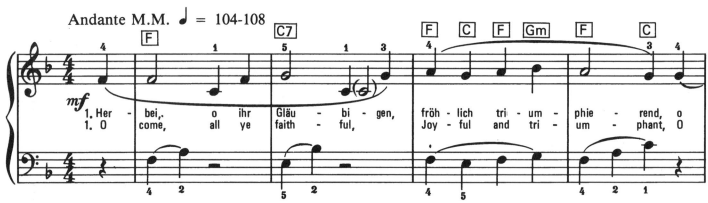

*) Anmerkung für den Lehrer: In der englischen Version ist der Ton C als halbe Note zu spielen.
*) Note for the teacher: In the English language version the note C is to be played as minim.

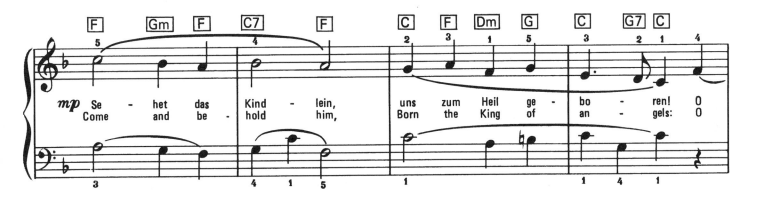

mp Sehet das Kindlein, uns zum Heil geboren! O
Come and behold him, Born the King of angels: O

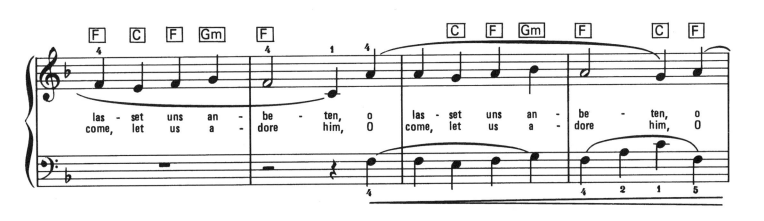

lasset uns anbeten, o lasset uns anbeten, o
come, let us adore him, O come, let us adore him, O

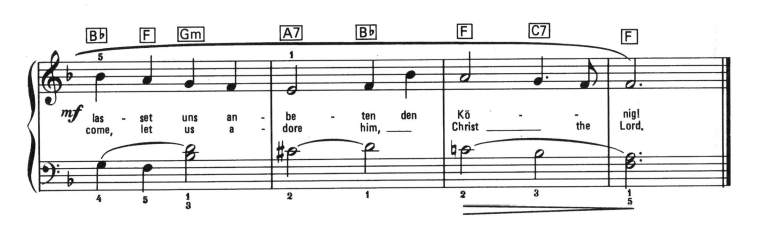

mf lasset uns anbeten den König!
come, let us adore him, ___ Christ ___ the Lord.

2. Kommt, singt dem Herren, o ihr Engelchöre,
frohlocket, frohlocket, ihr Seligen!
Ehre sei Gott im Himmel und auf Erden!
O lasset uns anbeten, o lasset uns anbeten,
o lasset uns anbeten den König!

3. O Herr, der du heute bist für uns geboren,
Herr Jesu, Ehre sei dir und Ruhm,
dir Fleisch geword'nes Wort des ew'gen Vaters!
O lasset uns anbeten, o lasset uns anbeten,
o lasset uns anbeten den König!

2. God of God, Light of Light,
Lo, he abhors not the Virgin's womb;
Very God, Begotten not created:
O come, let us adore him, O come, let us adore him,
O come, let us adore him, Christ the Lord.

3. Sing choirs of angels, Sing in exultation,
Sing, all ye citizens of heaven above:
'Glory to God in the highest:'
O come, let us adore him, O come, let us adore him,
O come, let us adore him, Christ the Lord.

Ihr Kinderlein kommet
O COME, LITTLE CHILDREN

Worte: Christoph von Schmid

Weise: Johann Abraham Peter Schulz (1780)
Arr.: Hans-Günter Heumann

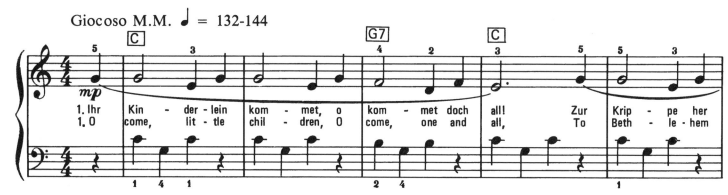

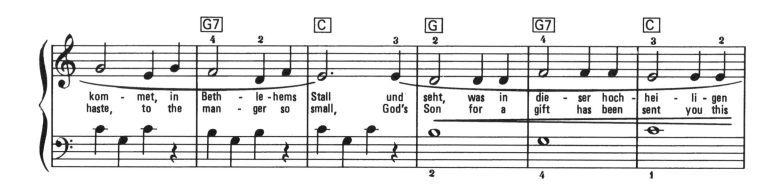

2. O seht in der Krippe
im nächtlichen Stall,
seht hier bei des Lichtes
hellglänzendem Strahl,
in reinlichen Windeln
das himmlische Kind,
viel schöner und holder
als Engel es sind.

3. Da liegt es, das Kindlein,
auf Heu und auf Stroh,
Maria und Josef
betrachten es froh;
die redlichen Hirten
knien betend davor,
hoch oben schwebt jubelnd
der Engelein Chor.

4. O beugt wie die Hirten
anbetend die Knie
erhebet die Händlein
und danket wie sie;
stimmt freudig, ihr Kinder
wer wollt' sich nicht freu'n,
stimmt freudig zum Jubel
der Engel mit ein.

2. O see, in the manger,
this strange little bed,
The Son, sweet and gentle,
is resting His head.
In swaddling clothes lying
so meek and so mild,
Yet purer than angels,
the heavenly Child.

3. On hay and on straw
in the manger He lies;
Both Mary and Joseph,
with fond loving eyes,
Are gazing upon it,
and shepherds draw near,
And jubilant angels
from heaven appear.

4. O kneel with the shepherds
in worshipful prayer,
And join the dear angels
who also are there;
Sing glory to God
in the heavens above,
And praise Him for Jesus,
the gift of His love.

Alle Jahre wieder

Worte: Wilhelm Hey

Weise: Friedrich Silcher (1842)
Arr.: Hans-Günter Heumann

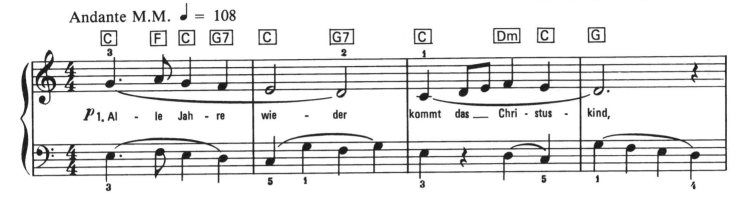

1. Alle Jahre wieder kommt das Christuskind,

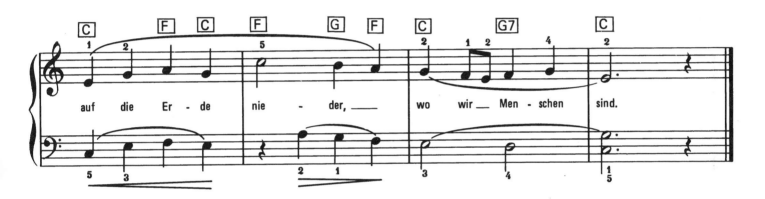

auf die Erde nieder, wo wir Menschen sind.

2. Kehrt mit seinem Segen ein in jedes Haus,
   geht auf allen Wegen mit uns ein und aus.

3. Ist auch mir zur Seite still und unerkannt,
   daß es treu mich leite an der lieben Hand.

Leise rieselt der Schnee

Worte und Weise: Eduard Ebel (1839-1905)
Arr.: Hans-Günter Heumann

Andante M.M. ♩ = 96-108

1. Lei - se rie - selt der Schnee,

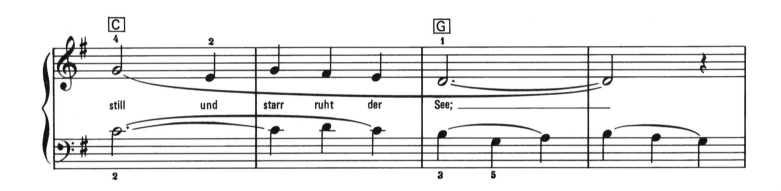

still und starr ruht der See;

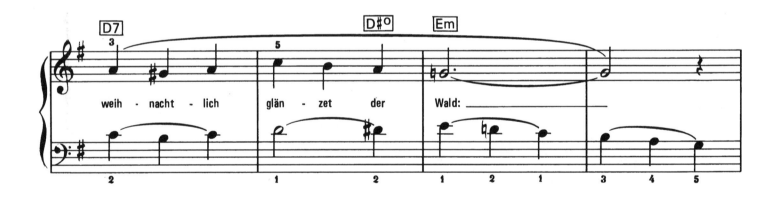

weih - nacht - lich glän - zet der Wald:

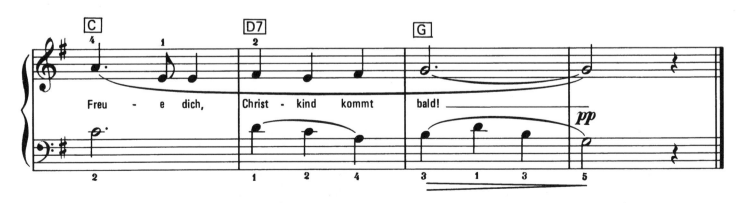

Freu - e dich, Christ - kind kommt bald!

2. In den Herzen ist's warm, still schweigt Kummer und Harm;
Sorge des Lebens verhallt: Freue dich, Christkind kommt bald!

3. Bald ist heilige Nacht, Chor der Engel erwacht;
hört nur wie lieblich es schallt: Freue dich, Christkind kommt bald.

Good Christian Men, Rejoice
IN DULCI JUBILO

Deutsche Weise aus dem 14. Jahrhundert
14th Century German Traditional
Arr.: Hans-Günter Heumann

2. Good Christian men, rejoice With heart and soul and voice;
Now ye hear of endless bliss: Joy! Joy! Jesus Christ was born for this!
He hath ope'd the heav'nly door, And Man is blessed evermore.
Christ was born for this! Christ was born for this!

2. Nun singet und seid froh, jauchzt alle und sagt so:
Uns'res Herzens Wonne liegt in der Krippe bloß
und leuchtet als die Sonne in seiner Mutter Schoß.
Du bist A und O, du bist A und O.

3. Good Christian men, rejoice With heart and soul and voice;
Now ye need not fear the grave: Peace! Peace! Jesus Christ was born to save!
Calls you one and calls you all, To gain His everlasting hall.
Christ was born to save! Christ was born to save!

3. Sohn Gottes in der Höh', nach dir ist mir so weh.
Tröst' mir mein Gemüte, o Kindlein, zart und rein,
und durch deine Güte, o liebstes Jesulein,
zeuch mich hin nach dir.

Good King Wenceslas

Words by J. M. Neale (1818-1866)

Piae Cantiones
Arr.: Hans-Günter Heumann

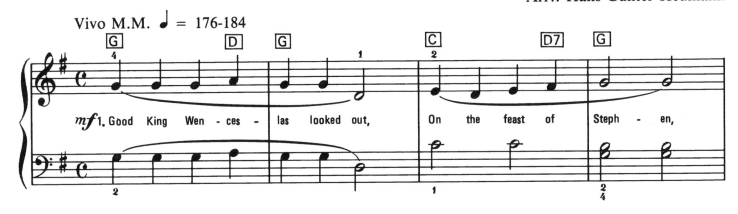

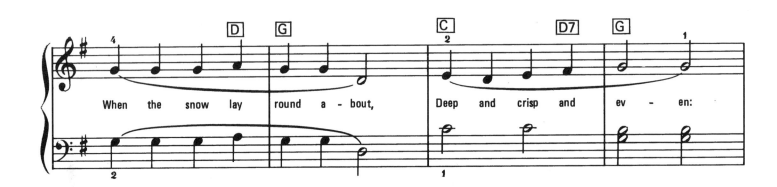

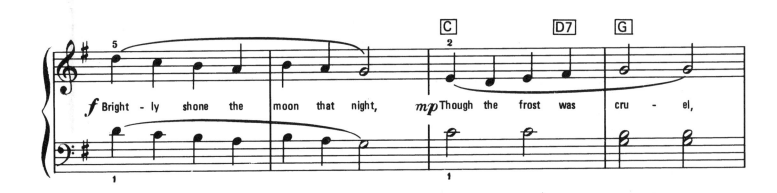

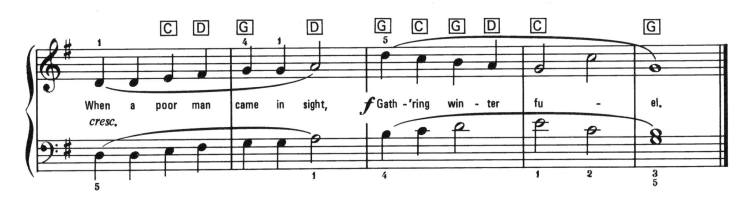

2. 'Hither, page, and stand by me,
   If thou knowest it, telling,
   Yonder peasant, who is he?
   Where and what his dwelling?'
   'Sire, he lives a good league hence,
   Underneath the mountain,
   Right against the forest fence,
   By St. Agnes' fountain.'

3. 'Bring me flesh and bring me wine,
   Bring me pine logs hither:
   Thou and I will see him dine,
   When we bear them thither.'
   Page and monarch, forth they went,
   Forth they went together;
   Through the rude wind's wild lament
   And the bitter weather.

4. 'Sire, the night is darker now,
   And the wind blows stronger;
   Fails my heart, I know not how;
   I can go no longer'.
   'Mark my footsteps good, my page;
   Tread thou in them boldly:
   Thou shalt find the winter's rage
   Freeze thy blood less coldly.'

5. In his master's steps he trod,
   Where the snow lay dinted;
   Heat was in the very sod
   Which the saint had printed.
   Therefore, Christian men, be sure,
   Wealth or rank possessing,
   Ye who now will bless the poor,
   Shall yourselves find blessing.

God Rest Ye Merry Gentlemen

Words: Wm. Sandys (1833)

Engl. Traditional
Arr.: Hans-Günter Heumann

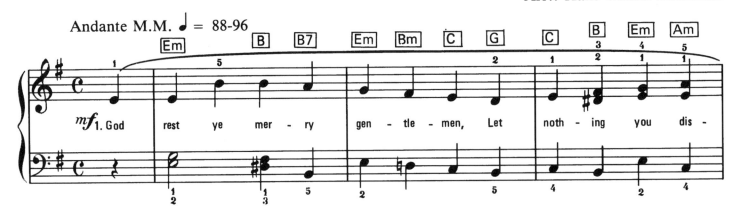

1. God rest ye mer - ry gen - tle - men, Let noth - ing you dis -

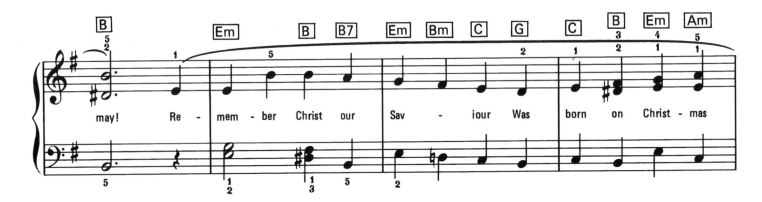

may! Re - mem - ber Christ our Sav - iour Was born on Christ - mas

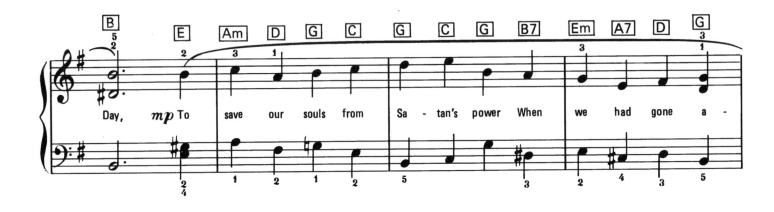

Day, To save our souls from Sa - tan's power When we had gone a -

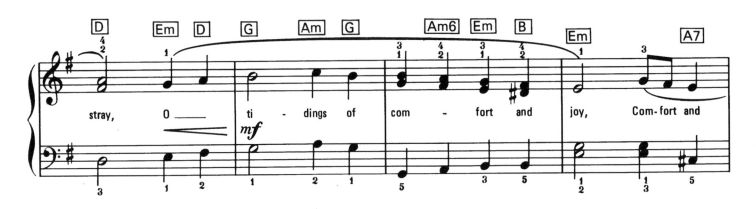

stray, O _____ ti - dings of com - fort and joy, Com - fort and

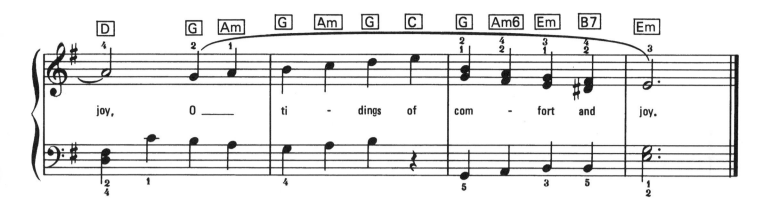

joy, O ___ ti - dings of com - fort and joy.

2. In Bethlehem in Jewry
   This blessed Babe was born,
   And laid within a manger
   Upon this blessed morn,
   The which His Mother Mary
   Did nothing take in scorn:
   O tidings of comfort and joy, Comfort and joy,
   O tidings of comfort and joy.

3. From God our heavenly Father
   A blessed angel came,
   And unto certain shepherds
   Brought tidings of the same,
   How that in Bethlehem was born
   The Son of God by name:
   O tidings of comfort and joy, Comfort and joy,
   O tidings of comfort and joy.

4. 'Fear not' then said the angel,
   'Let nothing ye affright;
   This day is born a Saviour
   Unto a Virgin bright
   To free all ye who trust in Him
   From Satan's power and might:
   O tidings of comfort and joy, Comfort and joy,
   O tidings of comfort and joy.

5. The shepherds at these tidings
   Rejoiced much in mind,
   And left their flocks a-feeding
   In tempest, storm, and wind,
   And went to Bethlehem staightway
   The Son of God to find;
   O tidings of comfort and joy, Comfort and joy,
   O tidings of comfort and joy.

6. Now when they came to Bethlehem
   Whereat the Infant lay,
   They found Him in a manger
   Where oxen feed on hay;
   His Mother Mary kneeling down
   Unto the Lord did pray:
   O tidings of comfort and joy, Comfort and joy,
   O tidings of comfort and joy.

7. Now to the Lord sing praises
   All you within this place,
   And with true love and brotherhood
   Each other now embrace;
   This holy tide of Christmas
   All others doth deface:
   O tidings of comfort and joy, Comfort and joy,
   O tidings of comfort and joy.

Kommet, ihr Hirten!

Worte: Karl Riedel (1827-1888)

Weise aus Böhmen (1870)
Arr.: Hans-Günter Heumann

Andante M.M. ♩ = 104-108

1. Kom - met, ihr Hir - ten, ihr Män - ner und Frau'n,
kom - met, das lieb - li - che Kind - lein zu schau'n.

Chri - stus, der Herr, ist heu - te ge - bo - ren,

den Gott zum Hei - land euch hat er - ko - ren. Fürch - tet euch nicht!

2. Lasset uns sehen in Bethlehems Stall,
was uns verheißen der himmlische Schall,
was wir dort finden, lasset uns künden,
lasset uns preisen in frommen Weisen. Halleluja!

3. Wahrlich, die Engel verkündigen heut'
Bethlehems Hirtenvolk gar große Freud'!
Nun soll es werden Friede auf Erden,
den Menschen allen ein Wohlgefallen. Ehre sei Gott!

Kommet, ihr Hirten!

Worte: Karl Riedel (1827-1888)

Weise aus Böhmen (1870)
Arr.: Hans-Günter Heumann

Andante M.M. ♩ = 104-108

f/p 1. Kom - met, ___ ihr ___ Hir - ten, ___ ihr ___ Män - ner ___ und ___ Frau'n,
kom - met, ___ das ___ lieb - li - che ___ Kind - lein ___ zu ___ schau'n.

f Chri - stus, der Herr, ist heu - te ge - bo - ren,

p den Gott zum Hei - land euch hat er - ko - ren, Fürch - tet ___ euch ___ *mf* nicht!

2. Lasset uns sehen in Bethlehems Stall,
was uns verheißen der himmlische Schall,
was wir dort finden, lasset uns künden,
lasset uns preisen in frommen Weisen. Halluluja!

3. Wahrlich, die Engel verkündigen heut'
Bethlehems Hirtenvolk gar große Freud'!
Nun soll es werden Friede auf Erden,
den Menschen allen ein Wohlgefallen. Ehre sei Gott!

Laßt uns froh und munter sein

Nikolauslied aus dem Hunsrück
German Traditional for St. Nicholas' Day
Arr.: Hans-Günter Heumann

Giocoso M.M. ♩ = 132

1. Laßt uns froh und munter sein und uns

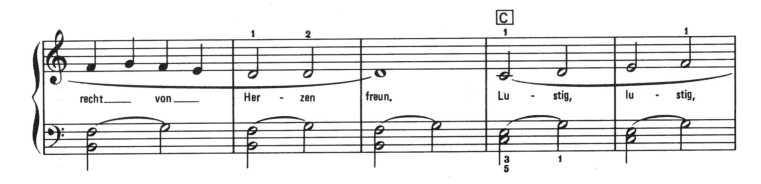

recht von Her-zen freun. Lu-stig, lu-stig,

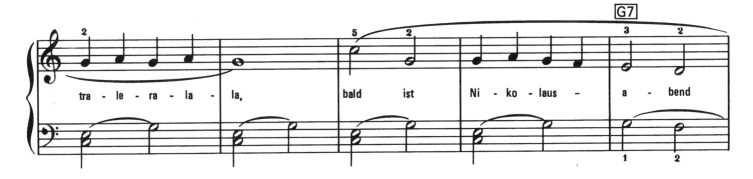

tra-le-ra-la-la, bald ist Ni-ko-laus- a-bend

da, bald ist Ni-ko-laus- a-bend da.

2. Bald ist uns're Schule aus,
dann ziehn wir vergnügt nach Haus.
Lustig, lustig...

3. Dann stell ich den Teller auf,
Niklaus legt gewiß was drauf.
Lustig, lustig...

4. Steht der Teller auf dem Tisch,
sing ich nochmals froh und frisch:
Lustig, lustig...

5. Wenn ich schlaf, dann träume ich:
Jetzt bringt Niklaus was für mich.
Lustig, lustig...

6. Wenn ich aufgestanden bin,
lauf ich schnell zum Teller hin.
Lustig, lustig...

7. Niklaus ist ein braver Mann,
den man nicht g'nug loben kann.
Lustig, lustig...

Inmitten der Nacht

Volksweise aus dem Kinzigtal (18. Jahrh.)
18th Cent. German Traditional
Arr.: Hans-Günter Heumann

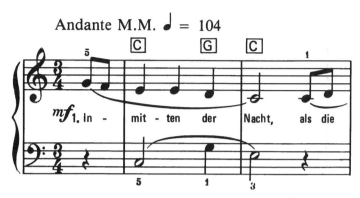

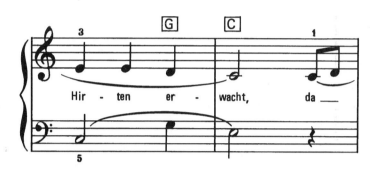

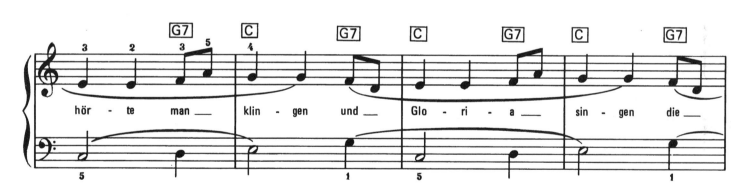

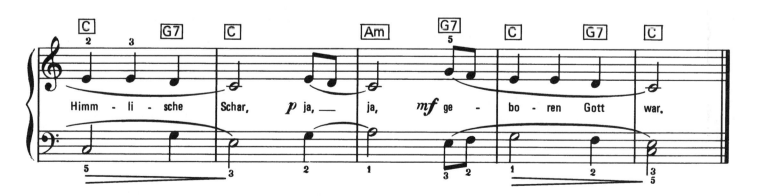

2. Die Hirten im Feld verließen ihr Zelt.
Sie gingen mit Eilen, ganz ohne Verweilen
dem Krippelein zu, ja, ja, der Hirt und der Bu.

3. Sie fanden geschwind das göttliche Kind.
Es herzlich zu grüßen, es zärtlich zu küssen
sie waren bedacht, ja, ja, die selbige Nacht.

B. & Co. 24 982

Hark! The Herald Angels Sing

Words by Charles Wesley

Music by Felix Mendelssohn-Bartholdy (1809-1847)
Arr.: Hans-Günter Heumann

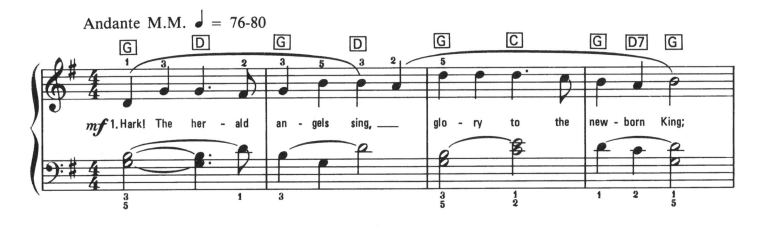

1. Hark! The her - ald an - gels sing, ___ glo - ry to the new - born King;

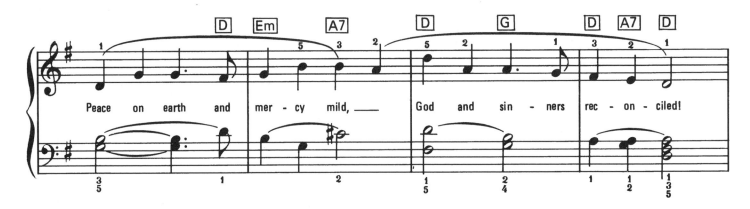

Peace on earth and mer - cy mild, ___ God and sin - ners rec - on - ciled!

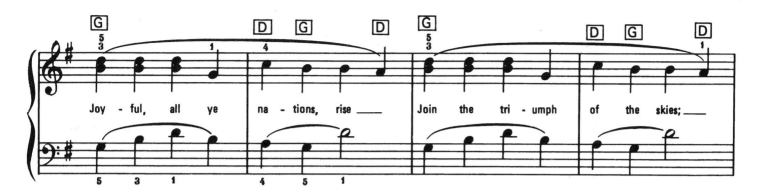

Joy - ful, all ye   na - tions, rise ____ Join the tri - umph   of the skies; ____

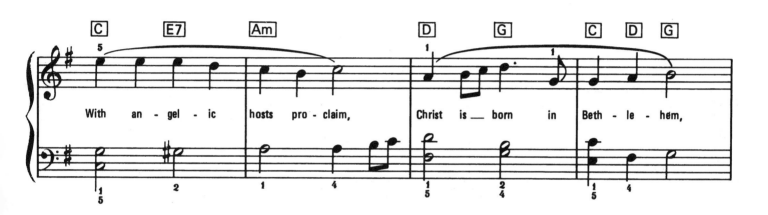

With an - gel - ic   hosts pro - claim,   Christ is __ born in   Beth - le - hem,

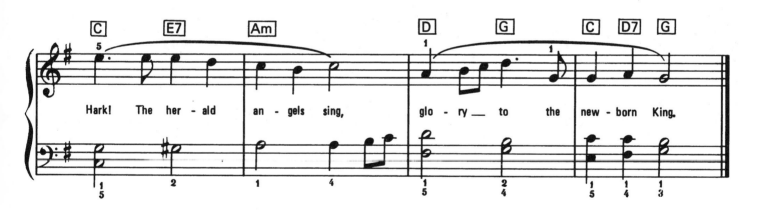

Hark! The her - ald   an - gels sing,   glo - ry __ to the   new - born King.

2. Christ, by highest heav'n adored;
   Christ, the everlasting Lord;
   Late in time behold Him come,
   Off-spring of a virgin's womb.
   Veiled in flesh the Godhead see;
   Hail the Incarnate Deity
   Pleased as Man with man to dwell
   Jesus our Emmanuel.
   Hark! The herald angels sing,
   glory to the newborn King.

3. Hail, the heav'n-born Prince of Peace!
   Hail, the Sun of Righteousness!
   Light and life to all He brings,
   Risen with healing in His wings,
   Mild He lays His glory by,
   Born that man no more may die,
   Born to raise the sons of earth,
   Born to give them second birth.
   Hark! The herald angels sing,
   glory to the newborn King.

Once in Royal David's City

Words by Mrs. Alexander (1823-1895)

Music by H.J. Gauntlett (1805-1876)
Arr.: Hans-Günter Heumann

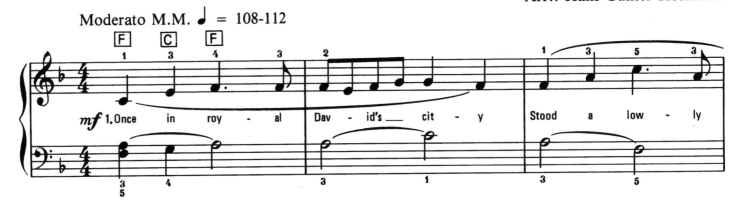

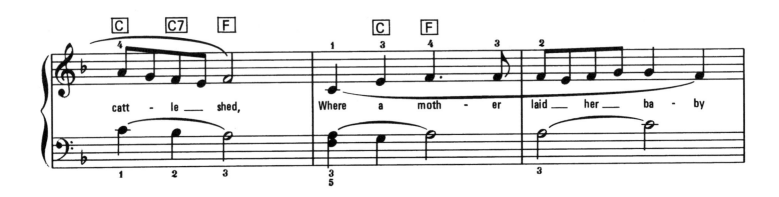

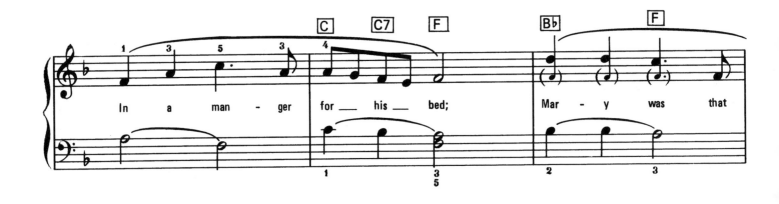

2. He came down to earth from heaven
Who is God and Lord of all,
And his shelter was a stable,
And his cradle was a stall;
With the poor and mean and lowly
Lived on earth our Saviour holy.

3. And through all his wondrous childhood
He would honour and obey,
Love and watch the lowly maiden,
In whose gentle arms he lay;
Christian children all must be
Mild, obedient, good as he.

4. For he is our childhood's pattern,
Day by day like us he grew,
He was little, weak, and helpless,
Tears and smiles like us he knew;
And he feeleth for our sadness,
And he shareth in our gladness.

5. And our eyes at last shall see him,
Through his own redeeming love,
For that child so dear and gentle
Is our Lord in heaven above;
And he leads his children on
To the place where he is gone.

6. Not in that poor lowly stable,
With the oxen standing by,
We shall see him; but in heaven,
Set at God's right hand on high;
When like stars his children crowned
All in white shall wait around.

B. & Co. 24 982

Go, Tell It on the Mountain

Trad. (Spiritual)
Arr.: Hans-Günter Heumann

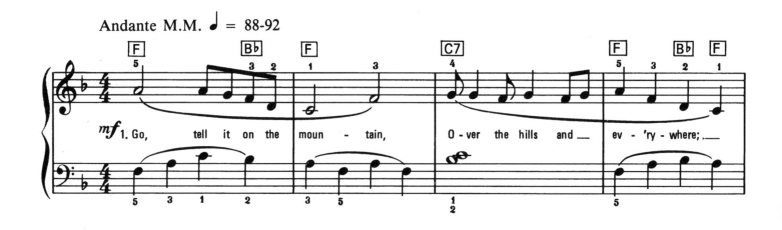

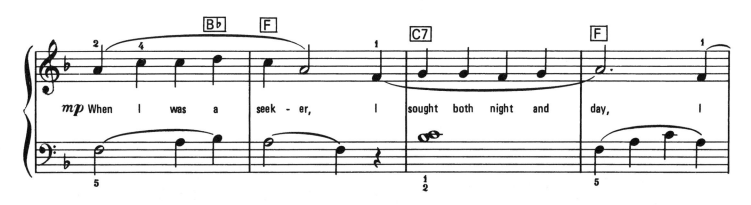

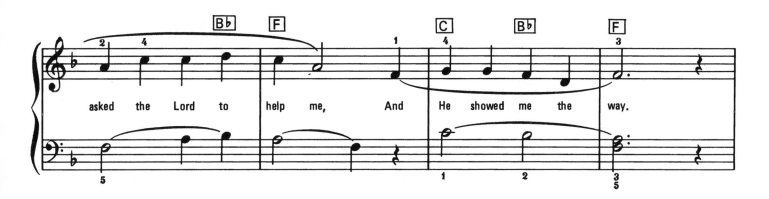

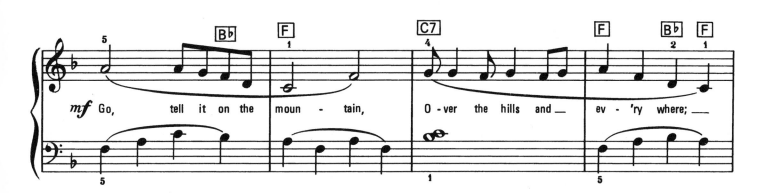

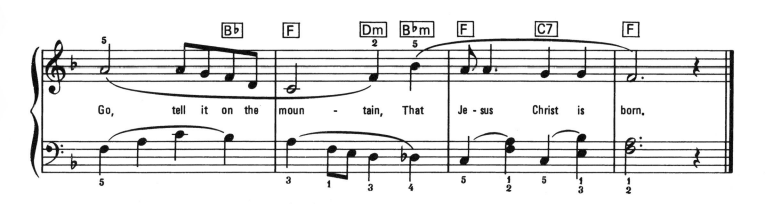

2. (Solist)
The shepherds feared and trembled
when lo above the earth
rang out the angel chorus
that hailed our Savior's birth.
(Chor) Go, tell it . . .

3. (Solist)
Down in a lonely manger
the humble Christ was born,
and God sent out salvation,
that blessed Christmas morn.
(Chor) Go, tell it . . .

Fröhliche Weihnacht überall

Deutscher Text: Chr. Fr. D. Schubart

Volksweise aus England/English Traditional
Arr.: Hans-Günter Heumann

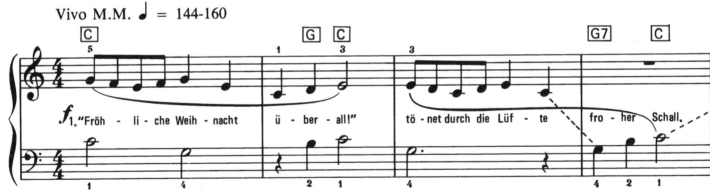

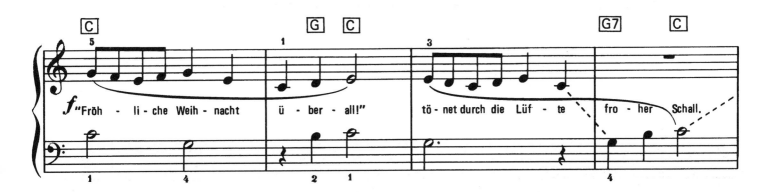

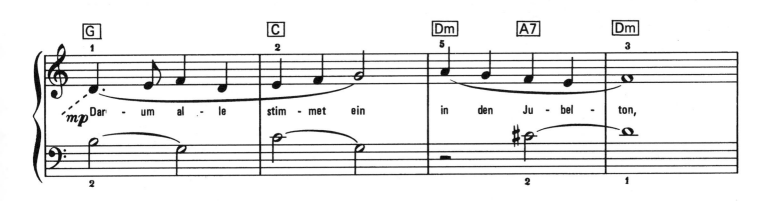

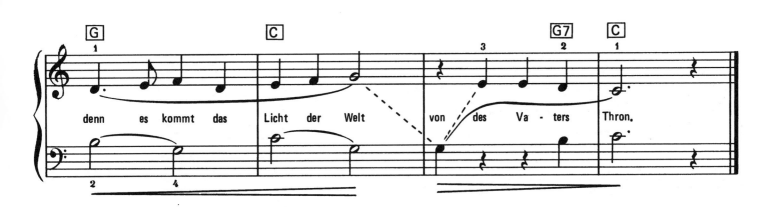

2. "Fröhliche Weihnacht überall!"
tönet durch die Lüfte froher Schall.
Weihnachtston, Weihnachtsbaum,
Weihnachtsduft in jedem Raum.
"Fröhliche Weihnacht überall!"
tönet durch die Lüfte froher Schall.

Licht auf dunklem Wege,
unser Licht bist du,
denn du führst, die dir vertrau'n,
ein zur sel' gen Ruh.

3. "Fröhliche Weihnacht überall!"
tönet durch die Lüfte froher Schall.
Weihnachtston, Weihnachtsbaum,
Weihnachtsduft in jedem Raum.
"Fröhliche Weihnacht überall!"
tönet durch die Lüfte froher Schall.

Was wir andern taten,
sei getan für dich,
daß bekennen jeder muß,
Christkind kam für mich.

Süßer die Glocken nie klingen

Worte: F. Wilhelm Kritzinger

Volksweise/ German Traditional
Arr.: Hans-Günter Heumann

Moderato M.M. ♩ = 112-116

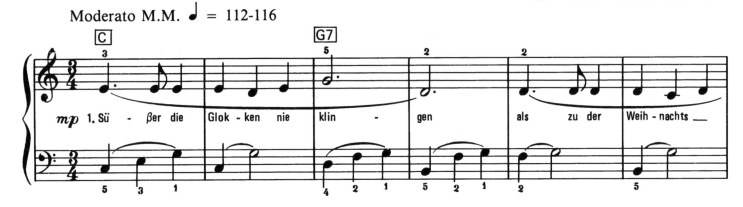

1. Sü - ßer die Glok - ken nie klin - gen als zu der Weih - nachts ___

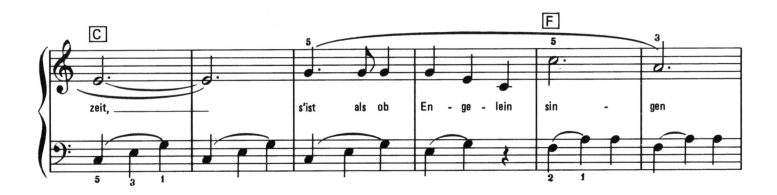

zeit, ___ s'ist als ob En - ge - lein sin - gen

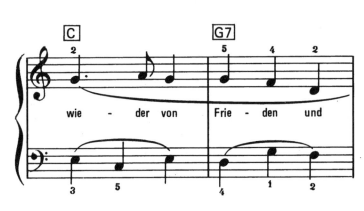

wie - der von Frie - den und

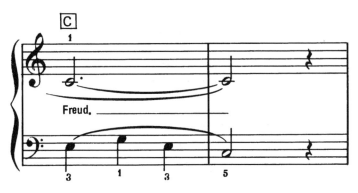

Freud.

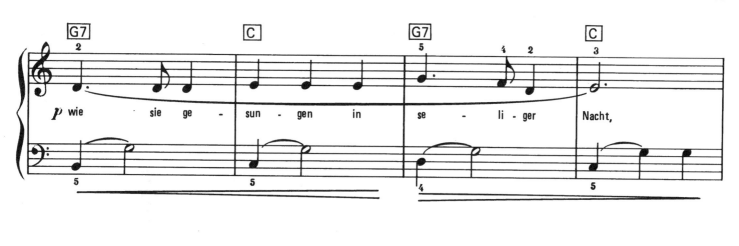

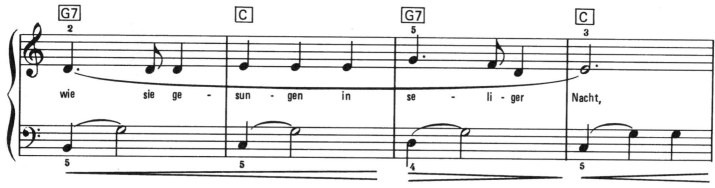

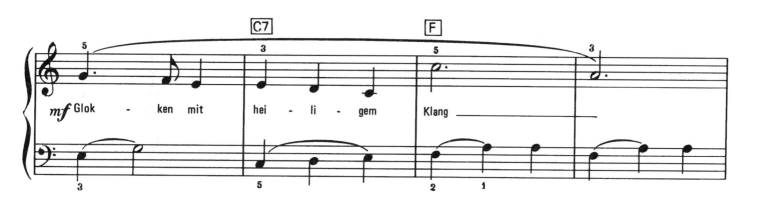

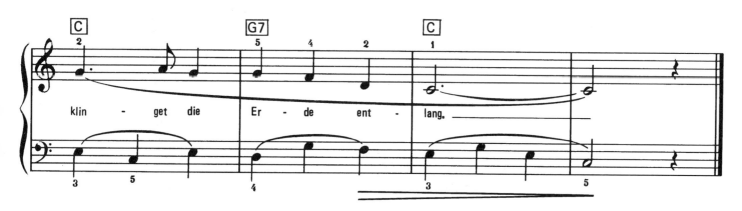

2. O, wenn die Glocken erklingen,
schnell sie das Christkindlein hört,
tut sich vom Himmel dann schwingen,
eilet hernieder zur Erd'
segnet den Vater, die Mutter, das Kind
segnet den Vater, die Mutter, das Kind
Glocken mit heiligem Klang
klinget die Erde entlang.

3. Klinget mit lieblichem Schalle
über die Meere noch weit,
daß sich erfreuen doch alle
seliger Weihnachtszeit.
Alle aufjauchzen mit einem Gesang
Alle aufjauchzen mit einem Gesang
Glocken mit heiligem Klang
klinget die Erde entlang.

The Holly and the Ivy

English Traditional
Arr.: Hans-Günter Heumann

Andante M.M. ♩ = 104-108

B. & Co. 24 982

2. The holly bears a blossom,
As white as the lily flower,
And Mary bore sweet Jesus Christ
To be our sweet Saviour:

Chorus: The rising of the sun etc.

3. The holly bears a berry,
As red as any blood,
And Mary bore sweet Jesus Christ
To do poor sinners good:

Chorus: The rising of the sun etc.

4. The holly bears a prickle,
As sharp as any thorn,
And Mary bore sweet Jesus Christ
On Christmas day in the morn:

Chorus: The rising of the sun etc.

5. The holly bears a bark,
As bitter as any gall,
And Mary bore sweet Jesus Christ
For to redeem us all:

Chorus: The rising of the sun etc.

6. The holly and the ivy,
When they are both full grown,
Of all the trees that are in the wood,
The holly bears the crown:

Chorus: The rising of the sun etc.

Joy to the World

Words by Isaac Watts

Music by Georg Friedrich Händel (1685-1759)
Arr.: Hans-Günter Heumann

Giocondo M.M. ♩ = 138-144

mf 1. Joy to the world! The Lord is come; Let earth re-ceive her King; Let ev-'ry heart pre-pare Him room, And heav'n and na-ture sing, And heav'n and na-ture sing, And heav-en and heav-en and na-ture sing.

2. Joy to the world! the Saviour reigns;
Let men their songs employ;
While fields and floods, rocks, hills, and plains
Repeat the sounding joy,
Repeat the sounding joy,
Repeat the sounding joy.

3. He rules the world! with truth and grace,
And makes the nations prove
The glories of His righteousness,
And wonders of His love,
And wonders of His love,
And wonders of His love.

O Little Town of Bethlehem

Words by Bishop Brooks (1835-1893)

English Traditional
Arr.: Hans-Günter Heumann

Andante M.M. ♩ = 88-92

2. For Christ is born of Mary;
   And, gathered all above,
   While mortals sleep, the angels keep
   Their watch of wondering love.
   O, morning stars, together
   Proclaim the holy birth,
   And praises sing to God the King
   And peace to men on earth.

3. How silently, how silently,
   The wondrous gift is given!
   So God imparts to human hearts
   The blessings of his heaven.
   No ear may hear his coming;
   But in this world of sin,
   Where meek souls will receive him, still
   The dear Christ enters in.

4. O holy Child of Bethlehem,
   Descend to us, we pray;
   Cast out our sin, and enter in:
   Be born in us today.
   We hear the Christmas angels
   The great glad tidings tell:
   O come to us, abide with us,
   Our Lord Emmanuel.

Kling, Glöckchen, klingelingeling!

Worte: Karl Enslin (1814-1875)

Weise: Benedikt Widmann (1884)
Arr.: Hans-Günter Heumann

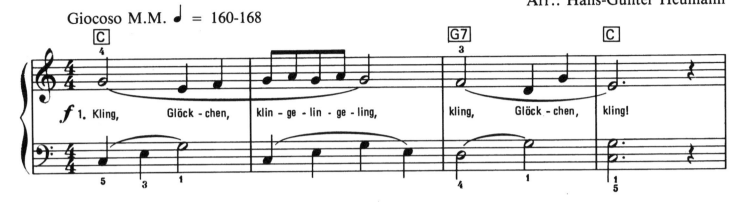

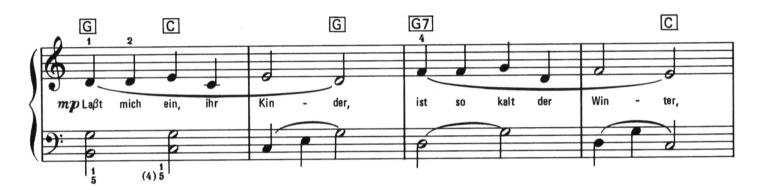

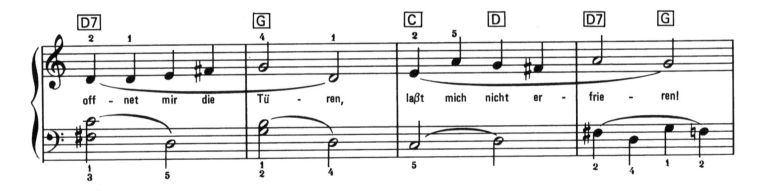

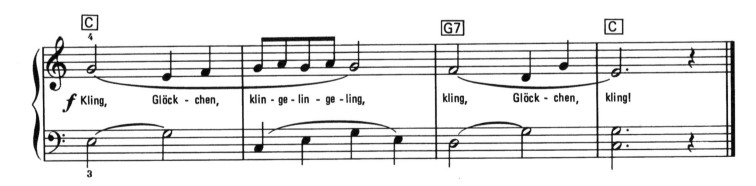

2. Kling, Glöckchen, klingelingeling, kling, Glöckchen, kling!
Mädchen hört und Bübchen, macht mir auf das Stübchen!
Bring euch milde Gaben, sollt euch dran erlaben!
Kling, Glöckchen, klingelingeling, kling, Glöckchen, kling!

3. Kling, Glöckchen, klingelingeling, kling, Glöckchen, kling!
Hell erglüh'n die Kerzen, öffnet mir die Herzen!
Will drin' wohnen frohlich, frommes Kind, wie selig!
Kling, Glöckchen, klingelingeling, kling, Glöckchen, kling!

B. & Co. 24 982

Am Weihnachtsbaum die Lichter brennen

Volksweise/German Traditional
Arr.: Hans-Günter Heumann

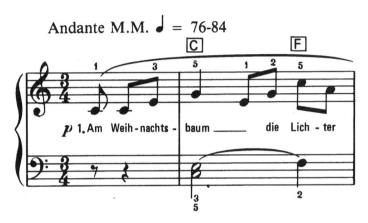

Andante M.M. ♩ = 76-84

p 1. Am Weih-nachts-baum _____ die Lich-ter

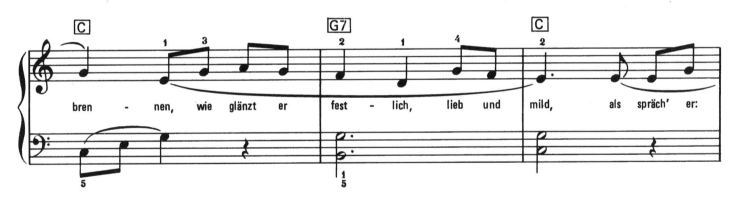

bren-nen, wie glänzt er fest-lich, lieb und mild, als spräch' er:

Wollt' _____ in mir er-ken-nen, ge-treu-er Hoff-nung stil-les Bild.

2. Die Kinder steh'n mit hellen Blicken,
das Auge lacht, es lacht das Herz;
o fröhlich seliges Entzücken!
die Alten schauen himmelwärts!

3. Zwei Engel sind hereingetreten,
kein Auge hat sie kommen sehn;
sie gehn zum Weihnachtstisch und beten
und wenden wieder sich und gehn.

4. Gesegnet seid ihr alten Leute,
gesegnet sei du kleine Schar!
Wir bringen Gottes Segen heute
dem braunen wie dem weißen Haar.

Schneeflöckchen, Weißröckchen

Deutsche Volksweise
German Traditional
Arr.: Hans-Günter Heumann

Moderato M.M. ♩ = 108

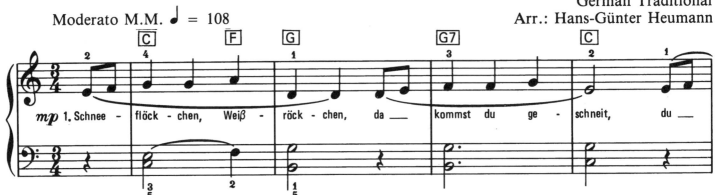

mp 1. Schnee - flöck - chen, Weiß - röck - chen, da ___ kommst du ge - schneit, du ___

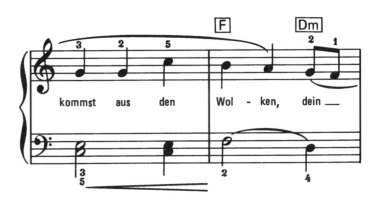

kommst aus den Wol - ken, dein ___

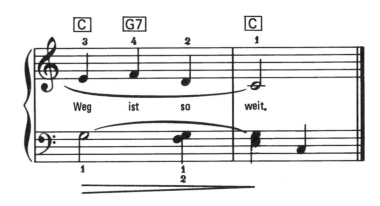

Weg ist so weit.

2. Komm, setz dich ans Fenster, du lieblicher Stern,
   malst Blumen und Blätter, wir haben dich gern.

3. Schneeflöckchen, du deckst uns die Blümelein zu,
   dann schlafen sie sicher in himmlischer Ruh.

4 Schneeflöckchen, Weißröckchen, komm zu uns ins Tal;
   dann bau'n wir den Schneemann und werfen den Ball.

Tochter Zion, freue dich!

Aus dem Oratorium "Judas Makkabäus"
From the Oratorio "Judas Macchabaeus"

Worte: Johann Joachim Eschenburg (1743-1820)

Georg Friedrich Händel (1685-1759)
Arr.: Hans-Günter Heumann

Allegretto M.M. ♩ = 120-132

D.C. al Fine

2. Hosianna, Davids Sohn! Sei gesegnet deinem Volk!
   Gründe nun dein ew'ges Reich! Hosianna in der Höh!
   Hosianna, Davids Sohn! Sei gesegnet deinem Volk!

3. Hosianna, Davids Sohn! Sei gegrüßet, König mild!
   Ewig steht dein Friedensthron, du, des ew'gen Vaters Kind!
   Hosianna, Davids Sohn! Sei gegrüßet, König mild!

Vom Himmel hoch, da komm ich her

SEHR LEICHT/
VERY EASY

Worte und Weise: Martin Luther (1483-1546)
Arr.: Hans-Günter Heumann

Espressivo M.M. ♩ = 144-152

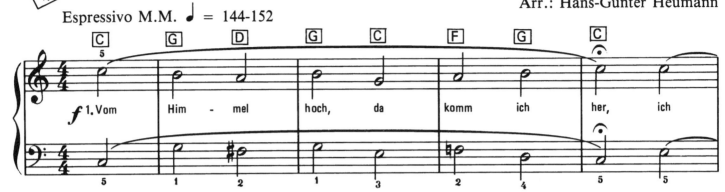

f 1. Vom Him - mel hoch, da komm ich her, ich

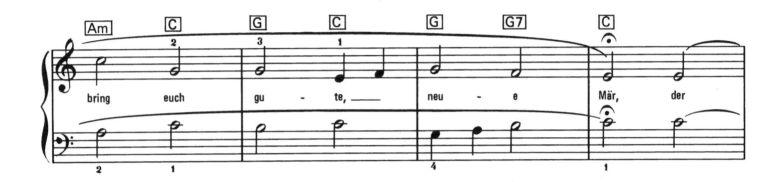

bring euch gu - te, _____ neu - e Mär, der

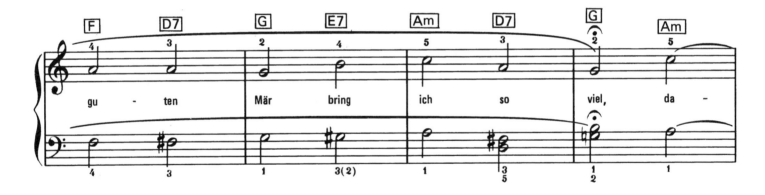

gu - ten Mär bring ich so viel, da -

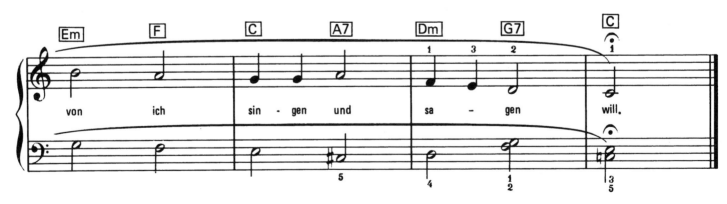

von ich sin - gen und sa - gen will.

2. Euch ist ein Kindlein heut' gebor'n,
von einer Jungfrau auserkor'n,
ein Kindelein so zart und fein,
das soll eu'r Freud' und Wonne sein.

3. Es ist der Herr Christ, unser Gott,
der will euch führ'n aus aller Not,
er will eu'r Heiland selber sein,
von allen Sünden machen rein.

4. Lob, Ehr' sei Gott im höchsten Thron,
der uns schenkt seinen eig'nen Sohn,
des freuen sich der Engel Schar
und singen uns solch neues Jahr.

Vom Himmel hoch, da komm ich her

Worte und Weise: Martin Luther (1483-1546)
Arr.: Hans-Günter Heumann

2. Euch ist ein Kindlein heut' gebor'n,
von einer Jungfrau auserkor'n.
ein Kindelein so zart und fein,
das soll eu'r Freud' und Wonne sein.

3. Es ist der Herr Christ, unser Gott,
der will euch führ'n aus aller Not,
er will eu'r Heiland selber sein,
von allen Sünden machen rein.

4. Lob, Ehr' sei Gott im höchsten Thron,
der uns schenkt seinen eig'nen Sohn,
des freuen sich der Engel Schar
und singen uns solch neues Jahr.

While Shepherds Watched

Words: Nahum Tate (1652-1715)

Este's Psalter (1592)
Arr.: Hans-Günter Heumann

Andante M.M. ♩ = 88-92

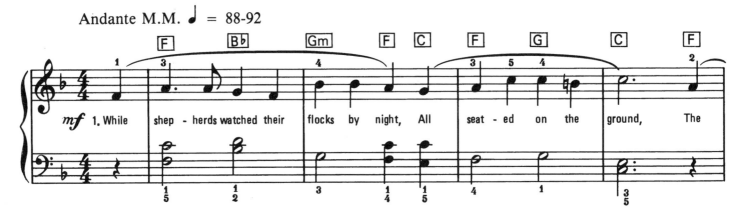

mf 1. While shep - herds watched their flocks by night, All seat - ed on the ground, The

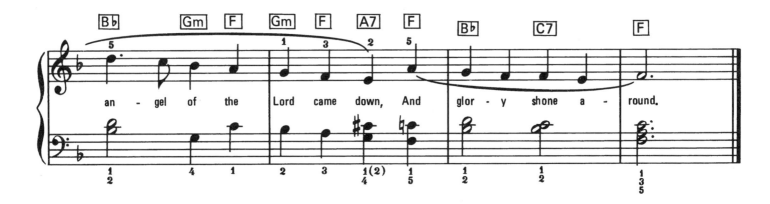

an - gel of the Lord came down, And glor - y shone a - round.

2. 'Fear not,' said he: for mighty dread
   Had seized their troubled mind;
   'Glad tidings of great joy I bring
   To you and all mankind.'

3. 'To you in David's town this day
   Is born of David's line
   A Saviour, who is Christ the Lord;
   And this shall be the sign:

4. 'The heavenly Babe you there shall find
   To human view displayed,
   All meanly wrapped in swathing bands,
   And in a manger laid.'

5. Thus spake the seraph; and forthwith
   Appeared a shining throng
   Of angels praising God, who thus
   Addressed their joyful song:

6. 'All glory be to God on high,
   And to the earth be peace;
   Good will henceforth from heaven to men
   Begin and never cease.'

Away in a Manger

Anon

Wm. J. Kirkpatrick (1838-1921)
Arr.: Hans-Günter Heumann

Moderato M.M. ♩ = 112-116

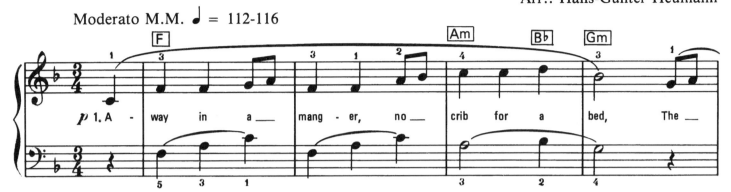

1. A - way in a mang - er, no crib for a bed, The

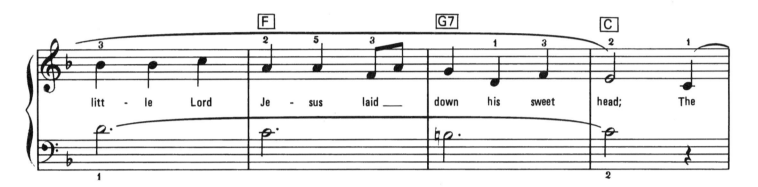

litt - le Lord Je - sus laid down his sweet head; The

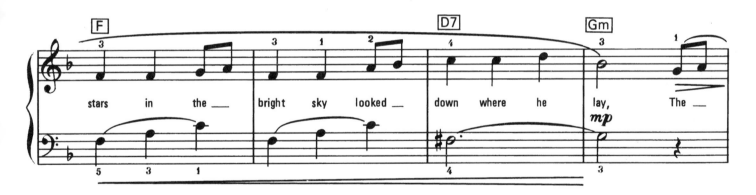

stars in the bright sky looked down where he lay, The

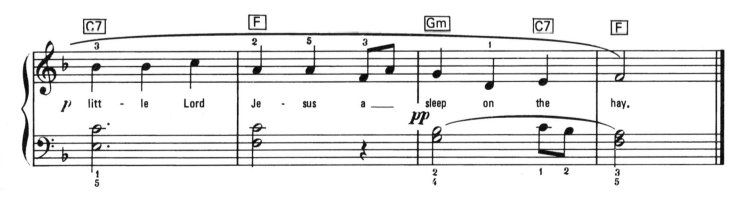

litt - le Lord Je - sus a sleep on the hay.

2. The cattle are lowing, the Baby awakes,
But little Lord Jesus, no crying he makes.
I love thee, Lord Jesus, look down from the sky,
And stay by my side till morning is nigh.

3. Be near me, Lord Jesus; I ask thee to stay
Close by me for ever, and love me, I pray.
Bless all the dear children in thy tender care,
And fit us for heaven to live with thee there.

Deck the Hall

Alte Waliser Volksweise
Old Welsh Folksong
Arr.: Hans-Günter Heumann

2. See the blazing Yule before us, Fa-la-la-la-la, la-la-la-la.
   Strike the harp and join the chorus, Fa-la-la-la-la, la-la-la-la.
   Follow me in merry measure, Fa-la-la, la-la-la-la.
   While I tell of Yuletide treasure, Fa-la-la-la-la, la-la-la-la.

3. Fast away the old year passes, Fa-la-la-la-la, la-la-la-la,
   Hail the new, ye lads and lasses, Fa-la-la-la-la, la-la-la-la.
   Sing we joyous all together, Fa-la-la, la-la-la, la-la-la.
   Heedless of the wind and weather, Fa-la-la-la-la, la-la-la-la.

We Wish You a Merry Christmas

Weise aus England/English Traditional
Arr.: Hans-Günter Heumann

Giocoso M.M. ♩ = 132-152

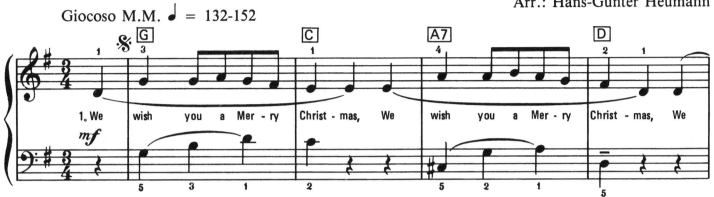

1. We wish you a Mer-ry Christ-mas, We wish you a Mer-ry Christ-mas, We

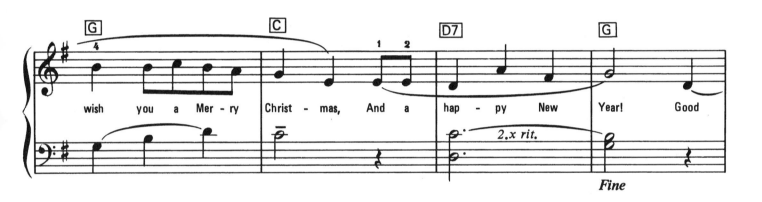

wish you a Mer-ry Christ-mas, And a hap-py New Year! Good

2.x rit.

Fine

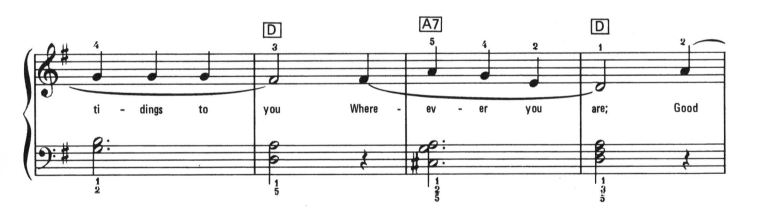

ti-dings to you Where-ev-er you are; Good

ti-dings for Christ-mas, And a hap-py New Year! We

D.S. al Fine

BoE 4057

HANS-GÜNTER HEUMANN

EASY PIANO ENTERTAINMENT

Beliebte Repertoire-Spielstücke in sehr leichter bis leichter Fassung für den modernen Klavierunterricht

For today's piano lesson: popular pieces in easy, if not the easiest, settings.

Barkarole / Andante grazioso / Prélude / When the Saints / Musette / Radetzky-Marsch / Zither-Ballade / Morning Has Broken / Wiegenlied / We Shall Overcome / Am Brunnen vor dem Tore / What Shall We Do with the Drunken Sailor / Melodie in F / Nun vergiß leises Flehn / Scarborough Fair / Santa Lucia / Down by the Riverside / Unter dem Sternenbanner / Brahms-Walzer / Rondo / All My Loving / Miniatur-Rondo / Menuett KV 6 / La Montanara / Wiener Blut / Whispering / Schwanensee / Amboß-Polka / Geschichten aus dem Wienerwald / Frühlingslied (Mendelssohn)

1

BOSWORTH EDITION